W
Like
to
Meet

Literary Characters

June Wentland

First published in Great Britain in 2016 by Southwick Press.

© Copyright 2016 by June Wentland.

A CIP record for this book is available from the British Library.

ISBN: 978-0-9558956-2-3

Running men illustrations by Simon Goodway.

Book design by John Maggs Design, Corsham.

Printed by Whitehall Printing, Bristol.

to

Florence Southwick

and to

Arthur Whipp

the grandparents I never met

and without whose romance

I would never have been born

and to Bertha and Robert White

the grandparents I knew and loved

Introduction

Stories are often inhabited by characters who are tragically thwarted in their search to find their soul mate or they're paired off by heartless authors into hopeless and unhappy relationships.

In the real world many people are increasing their chances of finding happiness by using dating columns or on-line sites.

Literary characters give us hours of enjoyment so it seems only fair that someone should give them the same opportunity.

Read the profiles and see if you can guess to which fictional characters they belong.

Hopefully you'll also find some characters you've never met before who'll lead you to new books and the beginning of some brand new and beautiful friendships. The heart keys at the beginning of the profiles give a clue to when each literary character was 'born'.

Turn to the end of the profiles section to gain a further clue and find the solution number for each character. Character answers are at the back of the book.

Heart Clues

 20th Century

 19th Century

 18th Century

 16th and 17th Century

 Pre 16th Century

 Myth / legend / folk / fairy tale / fairy story

1
Novel

Selective mute with a fondness for wearing black and abilities to see into the future WLTM someone with no plans for Christmas and a guilty past from which they can be guided towards redemption.

2

Novel

Uneducated man with no dress sense and prone to consuming jealousy WLTM his soul mate in the form of attractive, wayward lady to share near incestuous relationship, rambles across the freezing moors and a love that reaches beyond the grave.

3
Novel

Socially excluded man of high intelligence, low
self-esteem and complex personality problems
WLTM a lady to appreciate his sensitive side, his tales
of the Arctic and to either help him integrate into
human society or live in the wilds of South America.
A lack of conventional good looks is more than
made up for by height.

4
Play

Elderly gentleman of noble birth, recently estranged from his three daughters and with a new respect for the natural world WLTM a lady to help him overcome his dependence on flattery and support him through some mental health issues.

5
Novel

Rich European aristocrat with poor circulation problems, lack of self-image but with good teeth WLTM voluptuous red lipped ladies to share his atmospheric mansion which is set in an area abundant with unusual wildlife.

6
Novel

Deceitful young banker with a taste for embezzlement WLTM a young lady (with a friend conveniently susceptible to narcotic trances) and a large diamond which can help him juggle his debts and avoid insolvency.

7
Novel

Emotionally neglected lady with an aristocratic
and uptight husband WLTM a down to earth man
to sweep her off her feet into a life of sensuality
and so break asunder the chains of social class and
convention. Those interested should note that in
addition to unbridled ecstasy there will also be
some light gamekeeping duties.

8

Play

Ambitious Scots lady with a tendency to sleep walk
and with an obsessive compulsive disorder WLTM
a self-doubting, weak man to actively pursue an
upwardly mobile life-style.

9

Novels

Egocentric and eccentric bachelor with an illegal
substances habit and a reputed liking for hats WLTM
a partner to massage his ego, clean his apartment
and marvel at his powers of deduction.

10

Novella

Travelling salesman now confined to his bedroom
due to an unexpected and disfiguring transformation
WLTM an understanding girl with empathy for
large insects.

11
Novel

Young man from a Looked after Child background and with an appetite for second helpings WLTM a lady who will overlook his former involvement in young offending and share a happier future now that he has an adopted father.

12
Myth

Much misunderstood young man with a bad press
and a sight impairment due to an incident of self-
harm WLTM a lady who shares his sense of fate and
who will take a non-judgemental attitude towards his
former inappropriate feelings towards members of
his immediate family.

13
Novel

Ill-betrothed young woman with a palely clad
look-alike WLTM an arty young man proficient in
detective techniques to help restore her
sense of identity.

14
Novel

Former governess with a new found fortune
and a strong moral conscience WLTM a kindred
spirit for life long union of souls and telepathic
communication. A former inclination to polygamy
will not be viewed as an impediment.

15
Play

Controlling misogynist with no regard for
punctuality WLTM a shrewd woman willing to
tolerate chauvinistic behaviour in an attempt to find
an intellectual equal.

16

Folk tale and popular written version

Young widow with a lively sense of curiosity WLTM clean shaven young man with no former wives and no locked doors. Income is immaterial as the young lady inherited a large estate from her former husband who died from wounds inflicted by a sword.

17
Folk tale

Popular long haired lady with a sense of justice,
horse riding skills and who is not against a little
altruistic exhibitionism WLTM a kind man
who will not be too taxing.

18

Poem

Lonely woman with an unusual view of the world
and proficient weaving skills WLTM a handsome
gentleman who will reflect on life with her or
cure her of her curse.

19
Novel

Actress with a very protective brother WLTM a real prince charming free from the wicked influences of French fiction who will lock all known supplies of cyanide safely out of her reach and create with her a picture of happy domesticity while ageing gracefully.

20

Myth

Handsome young match maker with no love of his own but a beautifully furnished detached residence WLTM a beautiful young woman, who will not listen to mischief made by others or be afraid of his large white appendages.

21

Play

Attractive teenage girl condemned by controlling
parents to an arranged marriage WLTM handsome,
passionate and impulsive boy who is prepared
to dump his existing girlfriend and love
her to death.

22

Children's Story

Extremely slender lady WLTM gentleman with a firm head on his shoulders who appreciates a volatile nature. Red roses on the first date would be greatly appreciated but white roses will not be tolerated.

23
Novel

Elderly spinster with a very limited wardrobe and third degree burns WLTM a reliable gentleman who doesn't mind cobwebs, dust and stale cake and enjoys being humiliated.

24
Novel

Physically challenged, mature man with a
hearing impairment WLTM gypsy lady, preferably
accomplished in singing and dancing, to whom he
can show off his campanology skills and share cosy
nights in the belfry.

25
Novel

Wealthy, arrogant but good hearted 28 year old
Derbyshire man with a 21st Century fan club WLTM
intelligent and lively woman whose negative first
impressions will be overcome by his Colin Firth
looks and result in an improved appraisal of his
qualities leading to eventual marriage.

26

Poem

Insecure and egocentric Italian widower WLTM
aristocratic lady of similar social standing whose
heart will not be gladdened too easily, will
appreciate his sculptures and smile only for him.

27

Children's Novel

Widowed Yorkshireman with a manor house, orphaned niece from India and miraculously recovered son (who was previously always getting the hump) WLTM an understanding woman to share his recently unlocked garden and help love bloom once more in his heart.

28
Novel

Intelligent 20 year old carer with an inclination to matchmaking WLTM an older man with whom she can suddenly realise she is in love. Unattached male in-laws would be ideal.

29

Children's Novel

Kind daughter of a prison warden, with skills in creating disguises, WLTM meet a young man who like herself is sympathetic towards animals including headstrong amphibians.

30

Novel

Troubled medical practitioner with his own
laboratory and a strange potions habit WLTM
self-contained young lady who won't pry and will
accept volatile behaviour. A predilection towards
threesomes could be useful.

31

Fairy Story

Two sisters accustomed to getting their own way WLTM handsome gentleman with good promotion prospects. Potential suitors should value ambition above looks and shoe size.

32
Novel

Seafaring gentleman long deprived of female
company WLTM a lady with a boat and some free
time to meet up on Friday.

33

Fairy story

Manipulative or slow witted young womaniser with
an interest in climbing but apparently no ladder
WLTM a reclusive long haired lady with a wish to get
out more and experience of bondage.

34
Novel

Hastings boy committed to the battle against capitalism and to educating others from their false consciousness WLTM a girl who will help him show the workers on which side their bread is really buttered and to create their own surplus value in the form of equality and love.

35

Story in verse

Fun loving young woman in an unhappy marriage
to an older man WLTM a man with his sights set on
the stars to sweep her away from her run of the mill
relationship, flood her life with happiness and love
her from the bottom of his heart.

36
Novel

♥

Impressionable teenager and daughter of a country vicar with an over active imagination and a love of gothic novels WLTM a man with a large residence including some mysterious chambers and a father whom she can suspect of ghastly past deeds.

37
Novel

Intelligent, independent and newly wealthy Dorset
woman WLTM dashing but steadfast non-gambler
with a knowledge of farming. Prospective suitors
should not read too much into a Valentines card
and be brave enough to take on rival suitors, one of
whom owns a shot gun and is not afraid to use it.

38

Poem

Very elderly sea-going marksman with an unusual line in feathered accessories WLTM a woman who looks 'out of this world' and will wander the globe with him on his mission to educate others.

39

Children's Folk Rhyme

Young woman accustomed to hill walking and with strong arm muscles WLTM a sure footed boy who will provide her with a house with running water.

40
Play

Craftsman with a penchant for amateur dramatics
and the butt of someone else's joke WLTM a woman
who will be enchanted by him without the aid of
magic and join him in summertime songs
in the forest.

41
Novel

Man with a taste for travelling to remote nations of the world WLTM a woman to accompany him on his intrepid travels. She must be ready to meet misadventures both large and tiny.

42
Myth

Sun loving young man WLTM a non-ambitious girl
with a life guard's certificate to melt his heart but
keep his feet fixed firmly to the ground.

43

Story in verse

Young warrior who likes to fight fairly but becomes tetchy once crossed WLTM a loyal lady, preferably with a love of Swedish customs that extends beyond flat packed furniture. A life-long desire to be a queen of Germanic peoples would be an advantage as well as a knowledge of dragon repellents.

44
Fairy Story

Girl with a real sense of curiosity and a firm
understanding of her own likes and dislikes WLTM
a boy for early morning forest walks and guerrilla
breakfasting. He should be not too tall and not too
short, not too handsome and not too ugly
but just right.

45
Novel

Angelic and moralistic son of a vicar WLTM a chaste young woman with whom to start a new life in Brazil. Prospective suitors should keep any previous dark secrets to themselves.

46
Novel

Young woman with developed sensibilities and tired
of philanderers WLTM a reliable older bachelor
blessed with good sense.

47
Novel

Kind but unsophisticated daughter of a widowed
doctor living out in the provinces WLTM a reliable
old childhood friend and younger son of a Squire
who will come to realise that his feelings towards her
are more than platonic. Anyone wishing to obtain a
character reference can acquire one
from Aunt Harriet.

48
Play

University student temporarily interrupting his studies to sort out a few family problems WLTM a girl whom he can love enough to distract him from his rotten fortunes and help him cope with some disturbing supernatural manifestations.

49
Novel

Disinherited young man of German origins but
with Francophile leanings and a liking for making
incognito appearances at social gatherings WLTM
a Lady of similar lineage with whom he can
fall in love and annoy his father yet
further by thwarting his plans.

50

Children's Novel

Retired ex-sailor with a love of cheese WLTM a lady with rowing skills to meet him on his Caribbean island. Co-ordinates provided as well as the promise that an 'x' mark on paper means much more than just a kiss but moments to treasure.

51

Children's Folk Rhyme

Young woman with a liking for dairy products and the outdoors WLTM a man with whom to share outdoor snacking and who will protect her from encounters with unexpected arachnids.

52

Novel

Falsely accused elderly weaver with poor eyesight
formerly of Lantern Yard WLTM a lady of similar
age to share a modest cottage with him and
his golden haired adopted daughter.

53
Folk tale

Gentleman with a rather green approach to
establishing a fairer economy and with friends of a
happy disposition WLTM a woman who likes trees
to share his unconventional life style and proactive
approach to re-distributing wealth.

54
Children's Novel

Teenage girl with a taste for colourful petticoats,
now living on reduced means due to a miscarriage
of justice involving her father WLTM a nice young
man who can visit her by train as her home is
conveniently close to the railway. (Alight
at the station and look for the house with
three chimneys).

55

Fairy Story

Attractive young lady with an abusive in-law and a weakness for apples WLTM a young man of noble birth and of at least average height to awaken her to a rosy future.

56
Novel

Young west country lass with an unexpected family fortune and a complicated personal history WLTM a steadfast boy with whom she can have a romance on Exmoor. He should have his own coat of arms and be ready to save her from a forced marriage to an outlaw.

57

Story in verse

Brave young knight who is not averse to wearing articles of women's clothing (albeit in a rather unconventional fashion) WLTM a lady who will kiss him three times and present him with her life saving girdle.

58
Novel

Disillusioned Nottinghamshire woman WLTM a man who speaks the King's English and will not 'thee and thou' her but will mine the finer seams of her intellect to divert her from a controlling and destructive relationship with her son.

59

Story in verse

Greek girl with a love of singing, currently living in
Athens WLTM nobody but if she must be paired off
with someone may the gods make it a man who will
not be unhorsed and who loves her more
than any victory.

60
Novel

Young seaman and ex first mate of a passenger ship now lording it on a remote Malaysian island WLTM a compassionate woman who will forgive him for a past weakness and guard him from his own character flaws.

61
Play

28 year old man with fictitious younger brother,
dual identity and a strange former connection with a
handbag on Victoria Station WLTM his best friend's
cousin who will not think him trivial and will vow
undying love despite her mother's disapproval.

62

Fairy Story

Exhausted young woman with good family
connections but a powerful enemy WLTM an intrepid
young gentleman with a heavy duty strimmer and a
taste for extreme gardening whose handsome smile
and tender kiss will bring her round to the
idea of marriage.

63

Play

Italian army general WLTM a self-confident Venetian girl to woo with his stories, and secretly marry before embarking on an ill-fated 'honeymoon' to Cyprus.

64
Novel

Happily widowed mother and diarist with artistic talents (recently hiding in an Elizabethan mansion) WLTM a young farmer who although prone to jealousy will not treat her with cruelty or contempt.

65
Novel

Pleasant natured graduate of an Academy for Young
Ladies WLTM a heroic man deserving of her loyalty
and devotion who will not betray her in Brighton
with her cunning and opportunistic friend.

66

Fairy story

Retired lady recovering from a traumatic incident with a large furry mammal WLTM a man of similar age with whom to share walks in the wood and visits from her granddaughter.

67
Novel

Intelligent dark haired Lincolnshire girl with strong
rowing abilities and a bankrupt father WLTM a man
who is neither related to a family enemy nor the
suitor of her cousin, to fall in love with and live in an
area not liable to flooding.

68

Play

Low status German doctor with a dangerous thirst for knowledge, some dodgy dealings with the devil and an ill-advised taste for mischief WLTM a Greek woman of classical beauty to provide a diversion and inflame his passions as his time inexorably runs out.

69
Novel

Riverboat captain well-travelled in the Congo regions of Africa and explorer of the murky connotations of imperialism WLTM a woman with a strong moral compass with whom to reminisce while sailing on the Thames.

70
Myth

Happy and self-reliant young woman with excellent
spear throwing skills WLTM a man who can out run
her and be the apple of her eye without resorting
to tactics which would be banned by modern sports
events on the grounds of health and
safety regulations.

71
Novel

Easily influenced 27 year old daughter of a shallow
and money fixated baronet WLTM a former suitor
(now made good) who could sail back into her life,
be persuaded to propose to her a second time and
become the admiral of her affections.

72
Novel

Fair haired undercover cop WLTM a red head as
beautiful as the London Underground with whom to
ride off into a beautiful sunset and a surreal future.
A first date on a Thursday would be
particularly appropriate.

73
Play

Recently bereaved woman WLTM (in seven years'
time) a man brought to her by the sea. Prospective
dates are advised not to smile too incessantly or to
wear just what they will but to give careful thought
to their choice of stockings and cross garters.

74
Children's Folk tale

Deliciously handsome guy WLTM a woman with a
life time membership to weight watchers. She should
have a strong disinclination to eat confectionery
along with an exercise regime that includes
a passion for running.

75

Folk tale and Children's Poem

Tall German gentleman with unusual and colourful dress sense and a flair for playing wind instruments WLTM a woman to follow his lead, share in some subterranean adventures and be mother to his ever growing number of adopted children.

Key to solutions

Profile 1. See solution 34 – from *A Christmas Carol* by Charles Dickens (1843)

Profile 2. See solution 67 – from *Wuthering Heights* by Charlotte Bronte (1847)

Profile 3. See solution 12 – from *Frankenstein, or the Modern Prometheus* by Mary Shelley (1818)

Profile 4. See solution 64 – from *King Lear* by William Shakespeare (c.1600)

Profile 5. See solution 43 – from *Dracula* by Bram Stoker (1897)

Profile 6. See solution 51 – from *The Moonstone* by Wilkie Collins (1868)

Profile 7. See solution 29 – from *Lady Chatterley's Lover* by D.H. Lawrence (1928)

Profile 8. See solution 48 – from *Macbeth* by William Shakespeare (c.1603)

Profile 9. See solution 71 – from the *Sherlock Holmes* series by Arthur Conan Doyle (1880's – 1927)

Profile 10. See solution 26 – from *Metamorphosis* by Franz Kafka (1915)

Profile 11. See solution 50 – from *Oliver Twist* by Charles Dickens (1837)

Profile 12. See solution 59 – from *Oedipus*, Greek myth

Profile 13. See solution 27 – from *The Woman in White* by Wilkie Collins (1868)

Profile 14. See solution 33 – from *Jane Eyre* by Charlotte Bronte (1847)

Profile 15. See solution 9 – from *Taming of the Shrew* by William Shakespeare (c.1590)

Profile 16. See solution 22 – from *Bluebeard*, folk tale and best known written version by Charles Perrault (1697)

Profile 17. See solution 69 – from the *Lady Godiva*, British legend

Profile 18. See solution 45 – from *The Lady of Shalott* by Alfred Tennyson (c.1833)

Profile 19. See solution 3 – from *The Picture of Dorian Gray* by Oscar Wilde (1890)

Profile 20. See solution 57 – from *Eros*, Greek myth

Profile 21. See solution 38 – from *Romeo and Juliet* by William Shakespeare (c.1597)

Profile 22. See solution 1 – from *Alice's Adventures in Wonderland* by Lewis Caroll (1865)

Profile 23. See solution 60 – from *Great Expectations* by Charles Dickens (1860-1862)

Profile 24. See solution 75 – from *The Hunchback of Notre-dame* by Victor Hugo (1831)

Profile 25. See solution 7 – from *Pride and Prejudice,* by Jane Austen (1813)

Profile 26. See solution 44 – from *My Last Duchess* by Robert Browning (1842)

Profile 27. See solution 63 – from *The Secret Garden* by Frances Hodgson Burnett (1910)

Profile 28. See solution 24 – from *Emma* by Jane Austen (1816)

Profile 29. See solution 72 – from *The Wind in the Willows* by Kenneth Grahame (1908)

Profile 30. See solution 56 – from *The Strange Case of Dr Jekyll and Mr Hyde* by Louis Stevenson (1886)

Profile 31. See solution 37 – from *Cinderella,* fairy story

Profile 32. See solution 18 – from *Robinson Crusoe* by Daniel Defoe (1719)

Profile 33. See solution 2 – from *Rapunzel,* fairy story

Profile 34. See solution 19 – from *The Ragged Trousered Philanthropist* by Robert Tressell (1914)

Profile 35. See solution 73 – from *The Miller's Tale* by Geoffrey Chaucer (1300s)

Profile 36. See solution 20 – from *Northanger Abbey* by Jane Austen (1799)

Profile 37. See solution 39 – from *Far from the Madding Crowd* by Thomas Hardy (1874)

Profile 38. See solution 58 – from *The Rime of the Ancient Mariner* by Samuel Taylor Coleridge (1798)

Profile 39. See solution 74 – from *Jack and Jill,* English folk rhyme

Profile 40. See solution 4 – from *A Midsummer Night's Dream* by William Shakespeare (c.1596)

Profile 41. See solution 21 – from *Gulliver's Travels* by Jonathan Swift (1726)

Profile 42. See solution 40 – from *Icarus,* Greek myth

Profile 43. See solution 5 – from *Beowulf,* by unknown author (8th to 11th Century)

Profile 44. See solution 23 – from *Goldilocks,* fairy story

Profile 45. See solution 41 – from *Tess of the d'Urbevilles* by Thomas Hard (1891)

Profile 46. See solution 6 – from *Sense and Sensibility* by Jane Austen (1811)

Profile 47. See solution 42 – from *Wives and Daughters* by Elizabeth Gaskell (1865)

Profile 48. See solution 61 – from *Hamlet* by William Shakespeare (c.1602)

Profile 49. See solution 8 – from *Ivanhoe* by Sir Walter Scott (1820)

Profile 50. See solution 46 – from *Treasure Island* by Robert Louis Stevenson (1881)

Profile 51. See solution 10 – from *Little Miss Muffet*, Children's folk rhyme

Profile 52. See solution 28 – from *Silas Marner* by George Elliot (1861)

Profile 53. See solution 47 – from *Robin Hood*, British legend

Profile 54. See solution 65 – from *The Railway Children* by Edith Nesbit (1906)

Profile 55. See solution 11 – from *Snow White*, fairy story (Brothers Grimm version, 1812)

Profile 56. See solution 66 – from *Lorna Doone: A Romance of Exmoor* by Richard Doddridge (1869)

Profile 57. See solution 30 – from *Sir Gawain and the Green Knight*, by an unknown author (14th Century)

Profile 58. See solution 49 – from *Sons and Lovers* by D.H. Lawrence (1913)

Profile 59. See solution 31 – from *The Knight's Tale* by Geoffrey Chaucer (1300s)

Profile 60. See solution 13 – from *Lord Jim* by Joseph Conrad (1900)

Profile 61. See solution 32 – from *The Importance of Being Earnest* by Oscar Wilde (1895)

Profile 62. See solution 16 – from *The Sleeping Beauty,* fairy story

Profile 63. See solution 68 – from *Othello* by William Shakespeare (c.1603)

Profile 64. See solution 15 – from *The Tenant of Wildfell Hall* by Anne Bronte (1848)

Profile 65. See solution 52 – from *Vanity Fair: A novel without a hero* by William Makepeace Thackeray (1847)

Profile 66. See solution 70 – from *Little Red Riding Hood,* fairy story

Profile 67. See solution 53 – from *The Mill on the Floss* by George Elliot (1860)

Profile 68. See solution 17 – from *Doctor Faustus* by Christopher Marlowe (1604)

Profile 69. See solution 35 – from *Heart of Darkness* by Joseph Conrad (1899)

Profile 70. See solution 54 – from *Atlanta,* Greek myth

Profile 71. See solution 36 – from *Persuasion* by Jane Austen (1816)

Profile 72. See solution 55 – from *The Man Who Was Thursday* by G.K. Chesterton (1908)

Profile 73. See solution 62 – from *Twelfth Night* by William Shakespeare (c.1602)

Profile 74. See solution 25 – from *The Gingedrbread Man,* folk tale

Profile 75. See solution 14 – from *The Pied Piper of Hamlin,* folk tale and poem by Robert Browning (1842)

Solutions

1. The Queen of Hearts

2. The Prince

3. Sibyl Vine

4. Nick Bottom

5. Beowulf

6. Marianne Dashwood

7. Fitzwilliam Darcy

8. Wilfred of Ivanhoe

9. Petruchio

10. Little Miss Muffet

11. Snow White

12. Frankenstein's monster

13. Jim

14. The Pied Piper

15. Helen Graham

16. Sleeping Beauty

17. Dr Faustus

18. Robinson Crusoe

19. Frank Owen

20. Catherine Morland

21. Lemuel Gulliver

22. Bluebeard's wife

23. Goldilocks

24. Emma Woodhouse

25. The Gingerbread Man

26. Gregor Samsa

27. Laura Fairlie

28. Silas Marner

29. Constance Chatterley

30. Sir Gawain

31. Emily

32. John (Ernest) Worthing

33. Jane Eyre

34. The ghost of Christmas yet to come

35. Charles Marlow

36. Ann Elliott

37. The ugly sisters

38. Juliet of the House of Capulet

39. Bathsheba Everdene

40. Icarus

41. Angel Clare

42. Molly Gibson

43. Count Dracula

44. The Duke of Ferrara

45. The Lady of Shallot

46. Ben Gunn

47. Robin Hood

48. Lady Macbeth

49. Gertrude Morel (nee Coppard)

50. Oliver Twist

51. Godfrey Ablewhite

52. Amelia Sedley

53. Maggie Tulliver

54. Atalanta

55. Gabriel Syme

56. Henry Jekyll/ Mr Hyde

57. Eros

58. The Ancient Mariner

59. Oedipus

60. Miss Havisham

61. Prince Hamlet

62. Olivia

63. Archibald Craven

64. King Lear

65. Bobbie (Roberta) Waterbury

66. Lorna Doone

67. Heathcliffe

68. Othello

69. Lady Godiva

70. Red Riding Hood's grandmother

71. Sherlock Holmes

72. The gaoler's daughter

73. The Miller's wife Alison

74. Jill

75. Quasimodo

Author profile

Hull born author with an M.A. in Creative Writing and currently the Reader Development Officer for Bath and N.E. Somerset Library Service WLTM a male character with the passion of Heathcliffe, the intelligence of Sherlock Holmes, the looks and manners of Fitzwilliam Darcy and the focussed determination of the gingerbread man.